3 Write the tonic triad in each of the following keys.
Do *not* use key signatures, but remember to add any necessary sharp or flat sign

C000262689

A♭ major

E major

F minor

B♭ major

E minor

4 Rewrite this melody using notes of *half the value*. Remember to put in the new time signature at the place marked *.

10

Corelli

*

5 Describe each of the following harmonic intervals, giving the type and number (e.g. major 3rd, perfect 4th). The keys are named, and in each case the lower note is the key note.

10

G major

Type ....
Number ....

F major

Type ....
Number ....

C♯ minor

Type ....
Number ....

E♭ major

Type ....
Number ....

D minor

Type ....
Number ....

6 Write as semibreves (whole notes) the scales named below.

C harmonic minor, ascending, without key signature but including any necessary sharp or flat signs.

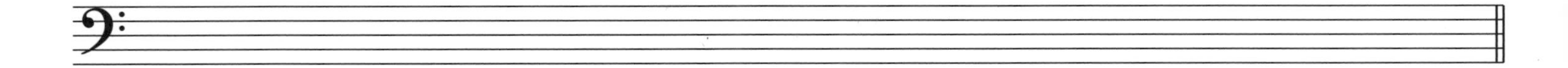

A major, descending, with key signature.

7 (a) Add the correct rest(s) at the places marked * to make each bar complete.

(b) Describe the time signature as: simple or compound ....

duple, triple or quadruple ....

Theory of Music Exams

GRADE 3

2009

Theory Paper Grade 3 2009 A

Duration 1½ hours

TOTAL MARKS 100

Candidates should answer ALL questions.
Write your answers on this paper – no others will be accepted.
Answers must be written clearly and neatly – otherwise marks may be lost.

1 Add the missing bar-lines to each of these *two* melodies, which both begin on the first beat of the bar.

10

2 Write a complete four-bar rhythm in $\frac{2}{4}$ time using the given opening, which begins on an upbeat.

10

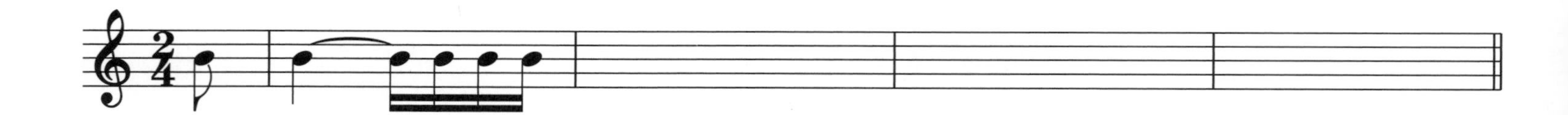

8 Look at this melody by Telemann and then answer the questions below.

Vivace ♩. = 104

(a) Give the meaning of each of these:

10

Vivace ....

♩. = 104 ....

f ....

– (e.g. bar 1) ....

‿ (bar 4) ....

(b) (i) This melody is in the key of D major. Draw a circle around a note which is the 7th degree of this scale.

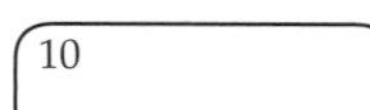

(ii) Which other key has the same key signature as D major? ....

(iii) Give the letter name of the *lowest* note in the melody. ....

(iv) How many demisemiquavers (32nd notes) is the first note of bar 2 worth? ....

(v) Answer TRUE or FALSE to this statement:
The widest melodic interval between two notes next to each other in this melody is a major 3rd. ....

(c) Write out the whole melody *an octave lower*, using the bass clef as shown.

10

Theory Paper Grade 3 2009 B

Duration 1 1/2 hours

TOTAL MARKS 100

Candidates should answer ALL questions.
Write your answers on this paper – no others will be accepted.
Answers must be written clearly and neatly – otherwise marks may be lost.

1 Add the time signature to each of these five melodies.

10

2 Write a complete four-bar rhythm in $\frac{9}{8}$ time using the given opening, which begins on an upbeat. Remember to complete the first whole bar.

10

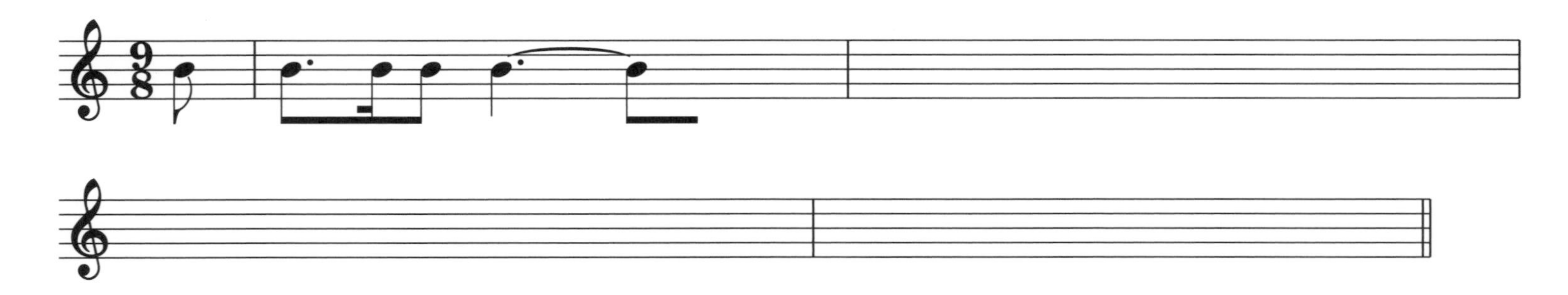

3 Transpose this melody *up* an octave, using the treble clef as shown.

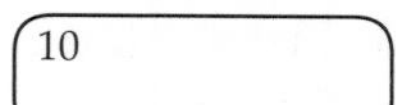

4 Write the key signature and tonic triad of each of the following keys.

10

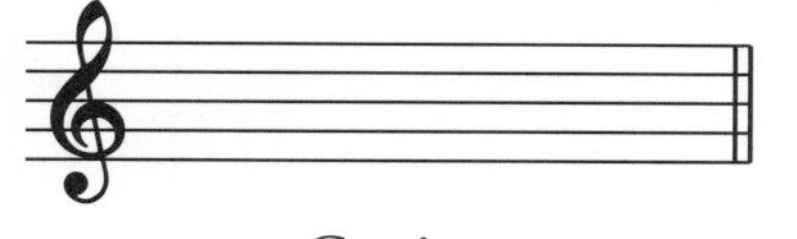

C minor

A♭ major

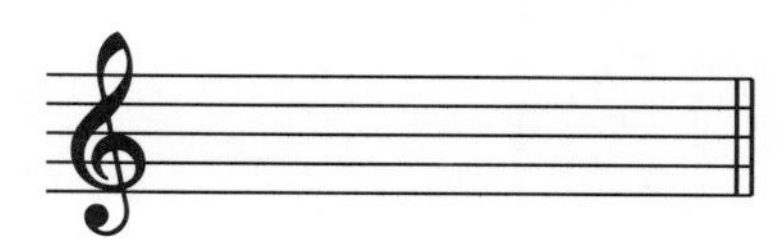

A major

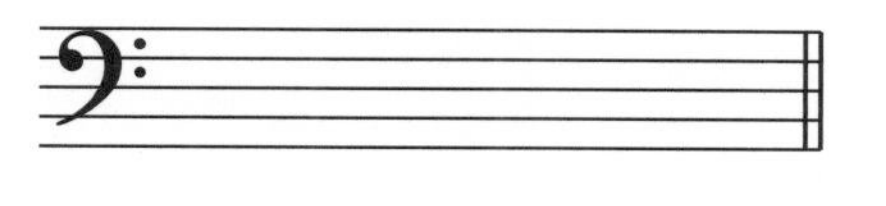

F♯ minor

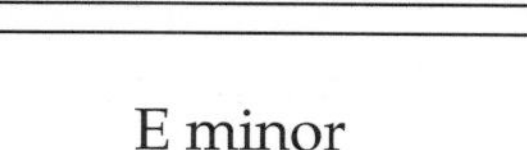

E minor

5 Name the key of each of the following scales. Where the key is minor, state whether the scale is in the harmonic or melodic form.

10

Key ....

Key ....

Key ....

Key ....

6 *After* each of these notes write a higher note to form the named *melodic* interval.
The key is G minor.

10

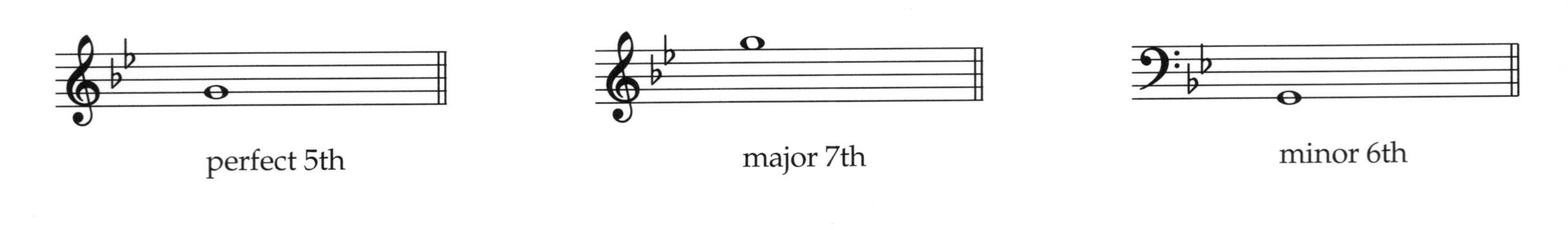

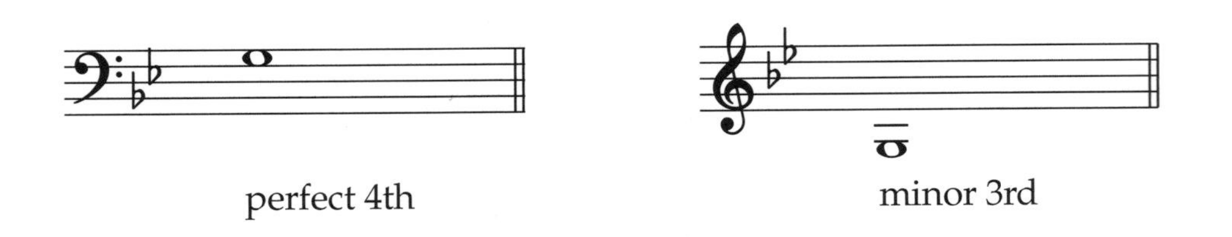

7 This melody by Dunhill contains *five* deliberate mistakes.
Rewrite it correctly on the given stave.

10

8 Look at this melody by Chopin and then answer the questions below.

(a) Give the meaning of each of these:

10

animato ....

♩ = 138 ....

the **3** in $\frac{3}{4}$ ....

riten. (bar 7) ....

marcato (bar 7) ....

(b) (i) What does the line over the first two notes (marked ↓) mean?

10

....

(ii) This melody is in the key of A minor. Draw a circle around a note which is the 6th degree of this scale.

(iii) How many demisemiquavers (32nd notes) is the first note of bar 3 worth? ....

(iv) How many times does the rhythm ♫ ♩ ♩ occur? ....

(v) Give the letter name of the *lowest* note in the melody. ....

(c) Write out the melody from the beginning of bar 5 to the end of the music using notes and a rest of *twice the value*. Remember to put in the new time signature at the place marked *.

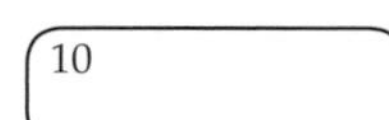

Theory Paper Grade 3 2009 C

Duration 1½ hours

Candidates should answer ALL questions.
Write your answers on this paper – no others will be accepted.
Answers must be written clearly and neatly – otherwise marks may be lost.

TOTAL MARKS
100

1 Add the missing bar-lines to each of these *two* melodies, which both begin on the first beat of the bar.

2 Write a complete four-bar rhythm in $\frac{4}{2}$ time using the given opening.

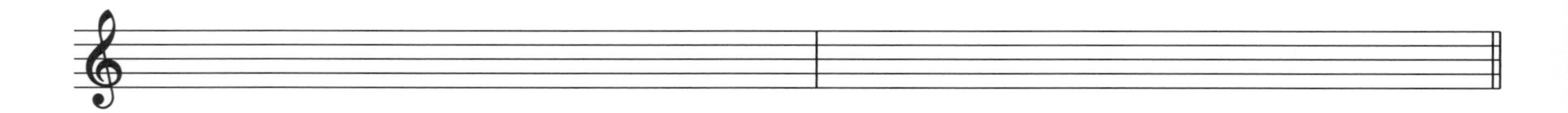

3 This melody contains *five* deliberate mistakes. Rewrite it correctly on the given stave.

10

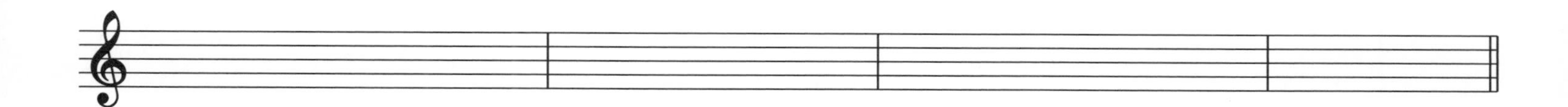

4 Add the correct rest(s) at the places marked * to make each bar complete.

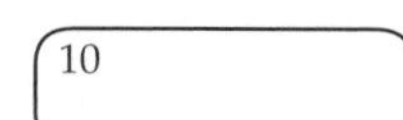

5 (a) Add the correct clef and any necessary sharp or flat signs to make the scale of A♭ major. Do *not* use a key signature.

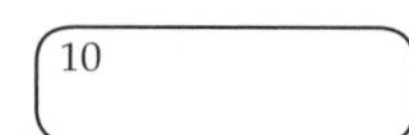

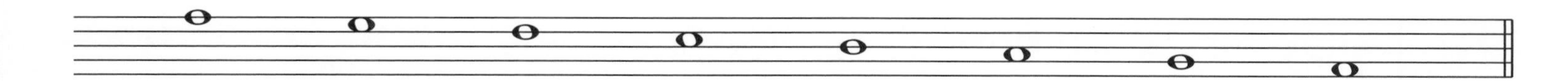

(b) Write as semibreves (whole notes) the scale of F♯ melodic minor, ascending, without key signature but including any necessary sharp or flat signs.

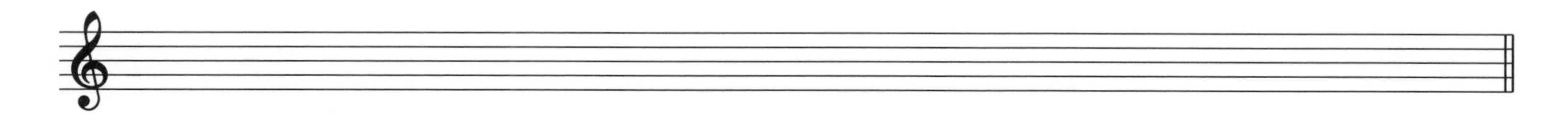

6 Describe each of these melodic intervals, giving the type and number (e.g. major 3rd, perfect 4th). The keys are named, and in each case the lower note is the key note.

10

G minor

Type ....

Number ....

A major

Type ....

Number ....

E major

Type ....

Number ....

C minor

Type ....

Number ....

F major

Type ....

Number ....

7 Name the key of each of these tonic triads.

10

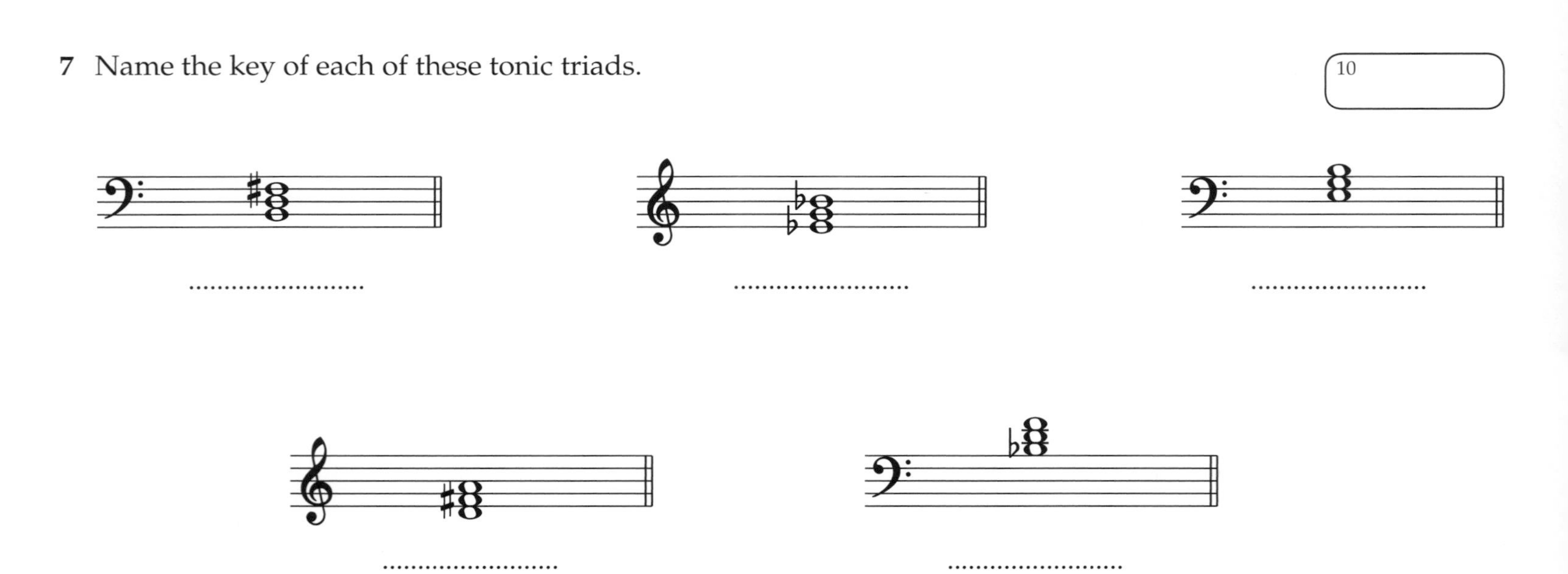

....

....

....

....

....

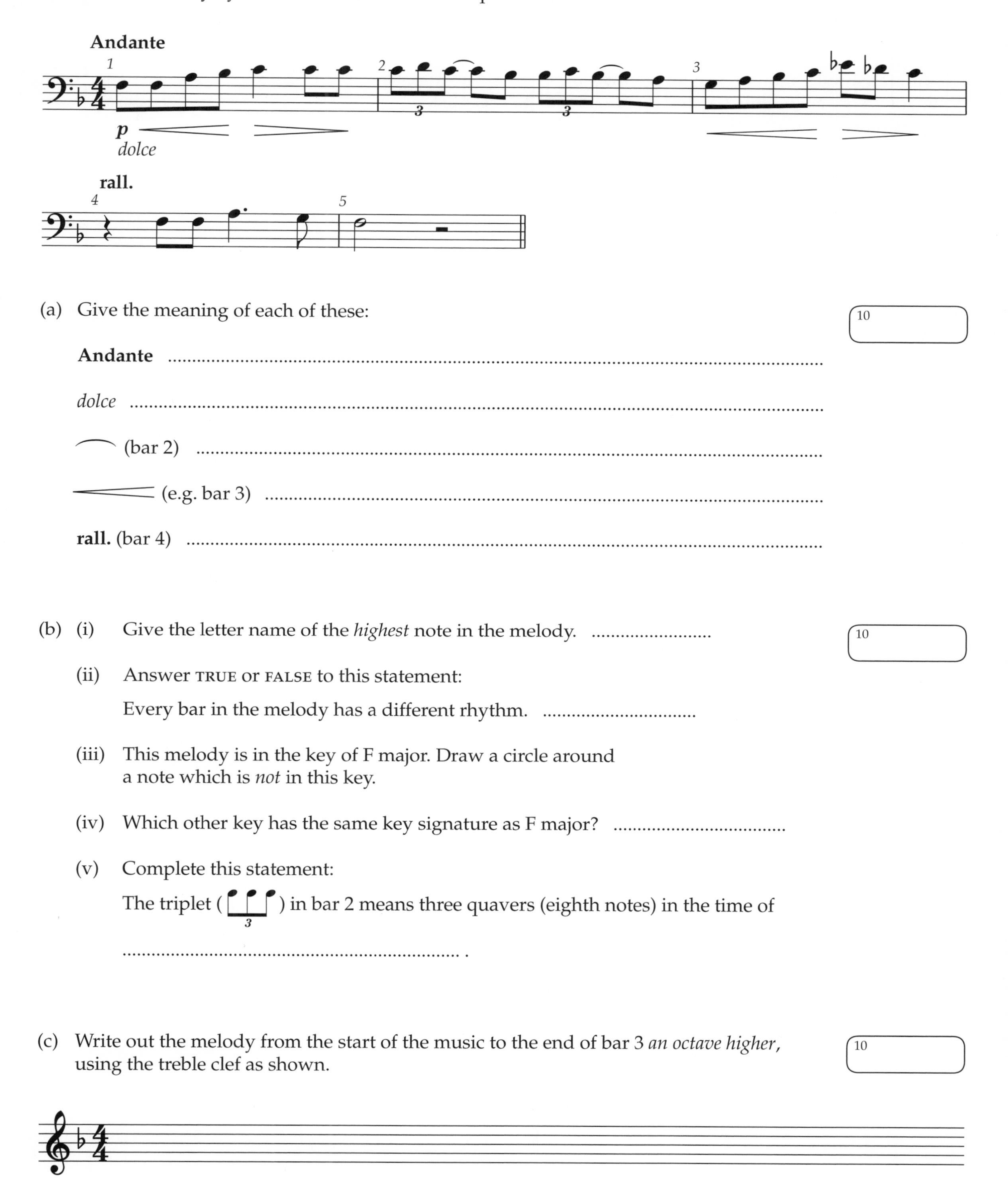

8 Look at this melody by Fauré and then answer the questions below.

(a) Give the meaning of each of these: 10

Andante ....

dolce ....

⌒ (bar 2) ....

< (e.g. bar 3) ....

rall. (bar 4) ....

(b) (i) Give the letter name of the *highest* note in the melody. 10

(ii) Answer TRUE or FALSE to this statement:

Every bar in the melody has a different rhythm. ....

(iii) This melody is in the key of F major. Draw a circle around a note which is *not* in this key.

(iv) Which other key has the same key signature as F major? ....

(v) Complete this statement:

The triplet (3) in bar 2 means three quavers (eighth notes) in the time of

....

(c) Write out the melody from the start of the music to the end of bar 3 *an octave higher*, using the treble clef as shown. 10

Theory Paper Grade 3 2009 S

Duration 1½ hours

TOTAL MARKS 100

Candidates should answer ALL questions.
Write your answers on this paper – no others will be accepted.
Answers must be written clearly and neatly – otherwise marks may be lost.

1 (a) Add the missing bar-lines to each of these *two* melodies, which both begin on the first beat of the bar.

10

Arutiunian

Boyce

(b) Describe the time signature of $\frac{3}{8}$ as: simple or compound ....

duple, triple or quadruple ....

2 Write a complete four-bar rhythm in $\frac{3}{4}$ time using the given opening.

10

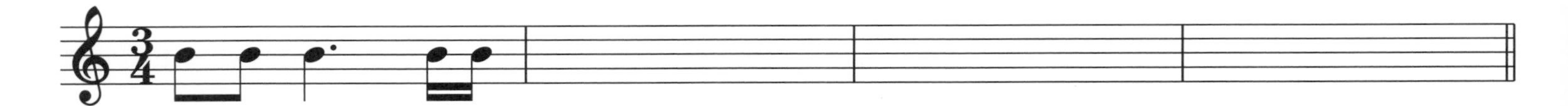

3 Add the correct clef and any necessary sharp or flat signs to each of these tonic triads. Do *not* use key signatures.

10

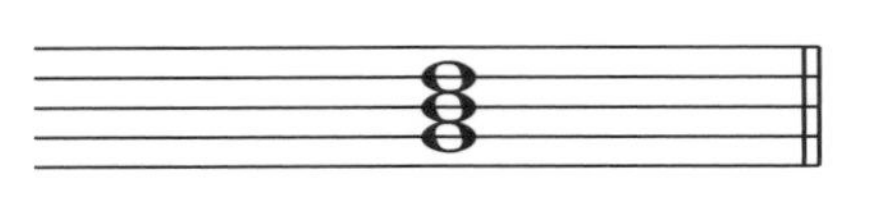

G minor

E major

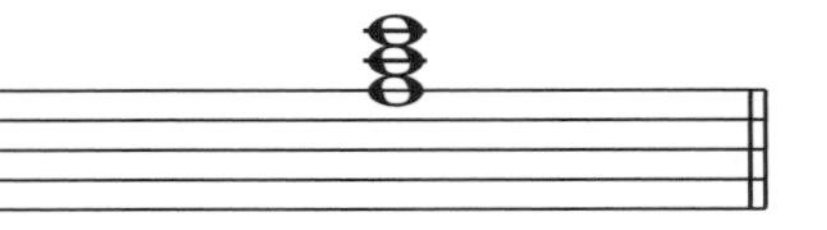

A major

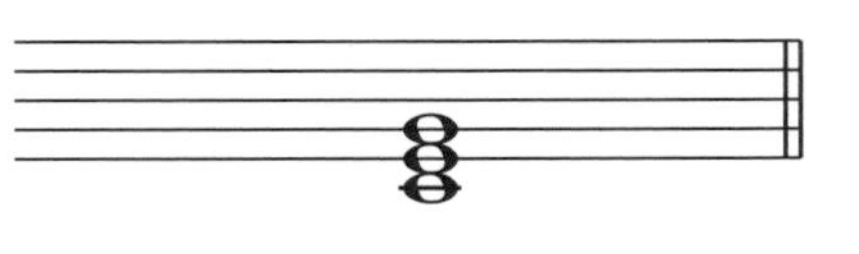

E minor

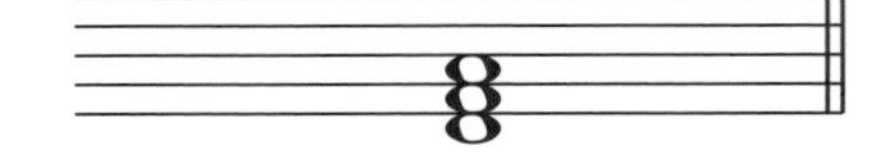

F major

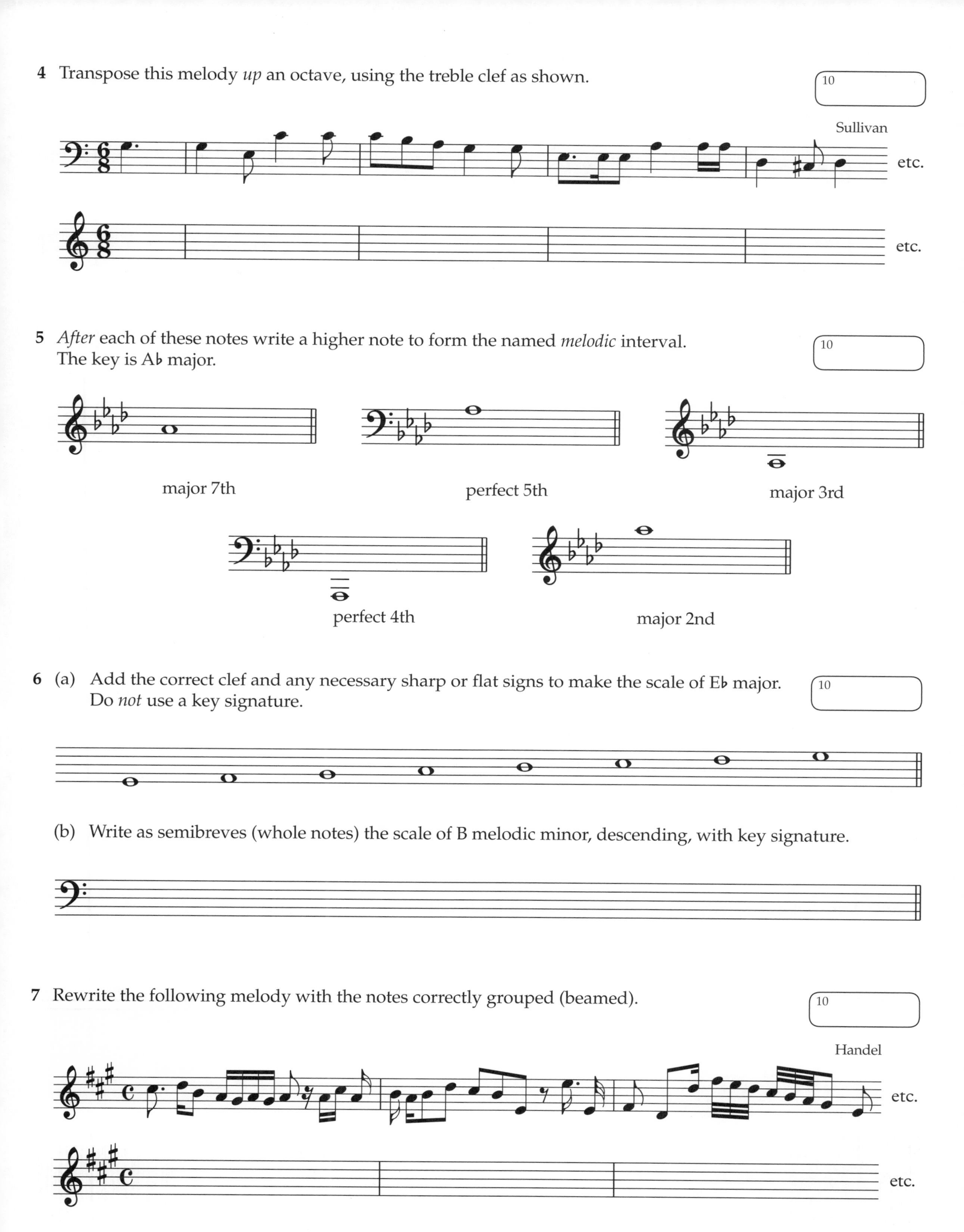
4 Transpose this melody *up* an octave, using the treble clef as shown.
10
Sullivan
etc.
etc.
5 *After* each of these notes write a higher note to form the named *melodic* interval.
The key is A♭ major.
10
major 7th
perfect 5th
major 3rd
perfect 4th
major 2nd
6 (a) Add the correct clef and any necessary sharp or flat signs to make the scale of E♭ major.
Do *not* use a key signature.
10
(b) Write as semibreves (whole notes) the scale of B melodic minor, descending, with key signature.
7 Rewrite the following melody with the notes correctly grouped (beamed).
10
Handel
etc.
etc.

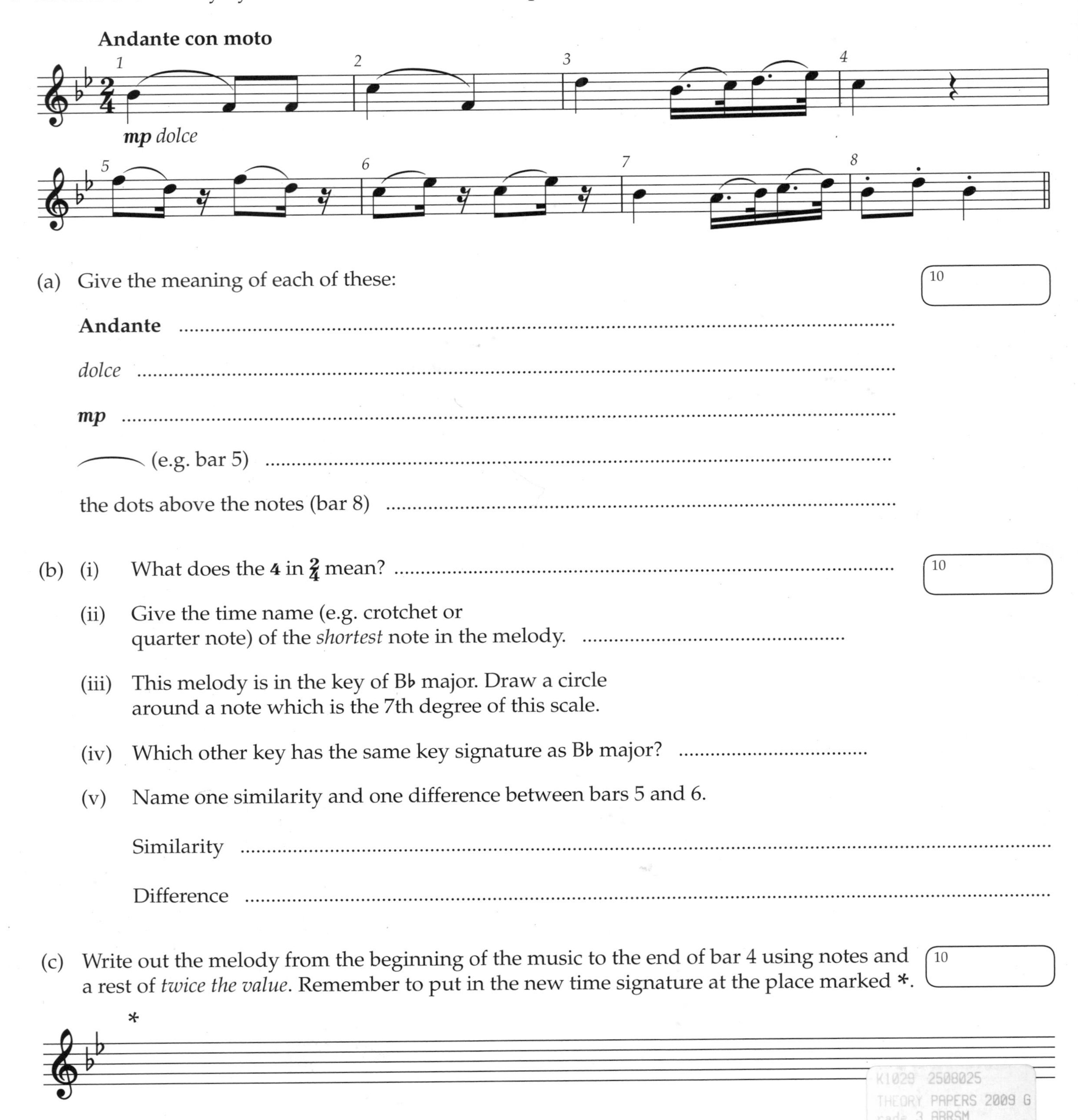

8 Look at this melody by Mozart and then answer the questions below.

(a) Give the meaning of each of these: | 10

Andante ....

dolce ....

mp ....

⁀ (e.g. bar 5) ....

the dots above the notes (bar 8) ....

(b) (i) What does the **4** in $\frac{2}{4}$ mean? .... | 10

(ii) Give the time name (e.g. crotchet or quarter note) of the *shortest* note in the melody. ....

(iii) This melody is in the key of B♭ major. Draw a circle around a note which is the 7th degree of this scale.

(iv) Which other key has the same key signature as B♭ major? ....

(v) Name one similarity and one difference between bars 5 and 6.

Similarity ....

Difference ....

(c) Write out the melody from the beginning of the music to the end of bar 4 using notes and a rest of *twice the value*. Remember to put in the new time signature at the place marked *. | 10

*

ABRSM
24 Portland Place
London W1B 1LU
United Kingdom

www.abrsm.org

Theory of Music Exams Model Answers, 2009, Grades 1 to 8 are available now from your usual retailer.

Published by ABRSM (Publishing) Ltd, a wholly owned subsidiary of ABRSM

Printed in England by Halstan & Co. Ltd, Amersham, Bucks 10/09

ISBN 978-1-84849-129-8